HUMPTY DUMPTY sat ON THE WALL

AND OTHER NURSERY RHYME SONGS

Published by Bonney Press,
an imprint of Hinkler Books Pty Ltd
45–55 Fairchild Street
Heatherton Victoria 3202 Australia
www.hinkler.com.au

BONNEY PRESS

© Hinkler Books Pty Ltd 2015

Illustrators: Steph Baxter, Sarah Coleman, Jon Contino, Sarah Dennis, Nicolò Giacomin & Lucia Calfapietra, Lauren Hom, Lalalimola, Mick Marston, Jess Matthews, Chris Robertson, Marie Simpson, Alice Stevenson, Yulia Vysotskaya

ISBN: 978 1 7436 3808 8

Printed and bound in China

Contents

Humpty Dumpty sat on the wall,
Humpty Dumpty had a great fall.
All the king's horses and all the king's men
Couldn't put Humpty together again.

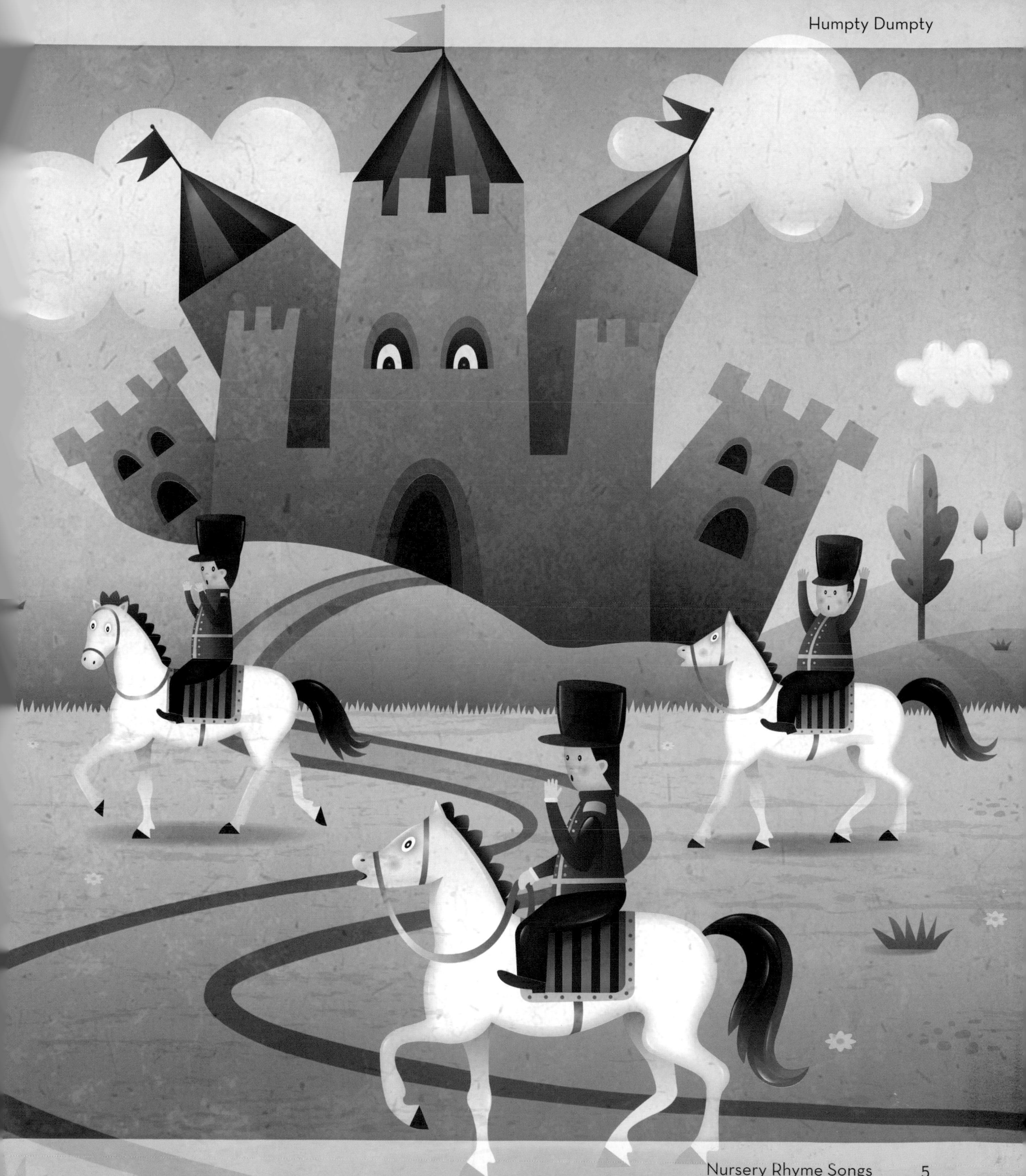

Yankee Doodle went to town
Riding on a pony;
He stuck a feather in his hat,
And called it macaroni.

MARY, MARY, QUITE CONTRARY HOW DOES YOUR GARDEN GROW? WITH SILVER BELLS AND COCKLE SHELLS, AND PRETTY MAIDS ALL IN A ROW.

It's raining, it's pouring.
The old man is snoring;
He went to bed and bumped his head,
And couldn't get up in the morning.

SING A SONG OF SIXPENCE
A POCKET FULL OF RYE;
FOUR AND TWENTY BLACKBIRDS,
BAKED in a PIE.
WHEN THE PIE WAS OPENED,
THE BIRDS BEGAN TO SING;
WASN'T THAT A DAINTY DISH,
TO SET BEFORE THE KING?

THE KING WAS IN HIS COUNTING-HOUSE,
COUNTING OUT HIS MONEY:
THE QUEEN WAS IN THE PARLOUR,
EATING BREAD AND HONEY.
THE MAID WAS IN THE GARDEN HANGING OUT THE CLOTHES,
when down came A BLACKBIRD,
AND PECKED OFF HER NOSE.

There was an old woman
Who lived in a shoe,
She had so many children,
She didn't know what to do;
She gave them some broth
Without any bread;
Then whipped them all soundly
And put them to bed.

Rub-a-dub dub,
Three men in a tub,
And who do you think they be?
The butcher, the baker,
The candlestick-maker.
Turn them out, knaves all three.

Sally, GO ROUND THE SUN
SALLY GO ROUND THE MOON
SALLY GO ROUND THE chimneypots
ON A SATURDAY AFTERNOON

Simple Simon met a pieman,
Going to the fair;
Said Simple Simon to the pieman,
'Let me taste your ware.'

Said the pieman to Simple Simon,
'Show me first your penny';
Said Simple Simon to the pieman,
'Indeed, I have not any.'

Simple Simon went a-fishing,
For to catch a whale;
All the water he had got,
Was in his mother's pail.

Simple Simon went to look
If plums grew on a thistle;
He pricked his fingers very much,
Which made poor Simon whistle.

He went for water in a sieve
But soon it all fell through;
And now poor Simple Simon
Bids you all adieu.

Oh, do you know the muffin man,
The muffin man, the muffin man,
Do you know the muffin man,
Who lives in Drury Lane?

Oh yes, I know the muffin man
The muffin man, the muffin man,
Yes, I know the muffin man,
Who lives in Drury Lane.

Jack and Jill went up the hill
To fetch a pail of water;
Jack fell down and broke his crown,
And Jill came tumbling after.

Up Jack got and home did trot,
As fast as he could caper;
He went to bed to mend his head
With vinegar and brown paper.

Row, row, row your boat,
Gently down the stream.
Merrily, merrily, merrily, merrily,
Life is but a dream.

Georgie Porgie, pudding and pie,
Kissed the girls and made them cry;
When the boys came out to play,
Georgie Porgie ran away.

Lucy Locket lost her pocket
Kitty Fisher found it
Not a penny was there in it
But a ribbon round it

Polly put the kettle on,
Polly put the kettle on,
Polly put the kettle on,
We'll all have tea.

Sukey take it off again,
Sukey take it off again,
Sukey take it off again,
They've all gone away.

Little Miss Muffet
Sat on a tuffet,
Eating her curds and whey;
Along came a spider,
Who sat down beside her
And frightened Miss Muffet away.

Hot cross buns!
Hot cross buns!
One a penny, two a penny,
Hot cross buns!

If you have no daughters,
Give them to your sons.
One a penny,
Two a penny,
Hot cross buns!

Oh... the grand old Duke of York,
He had ten thousand men,
He marched them up to the top of the hill
And he marched them down again.
And when they were up they were up,
And when they were down they were down;
And when they were only halfway up
They were neither up nor down.